"Oh, my gosh. Are you OK?
Which way is the ship?"

"Keep looking. She's here somewhere."

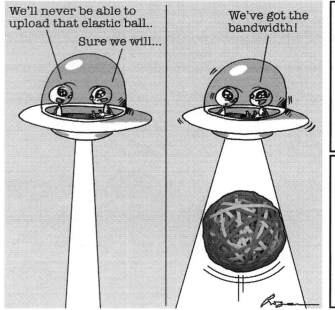

"I'm done being Keto."

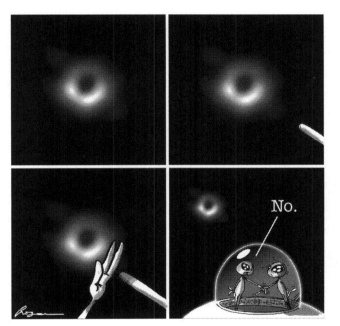

"Now, *these* designs are the cream of the crop-circles!"

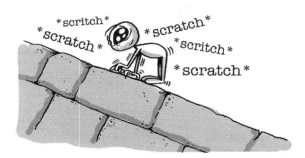

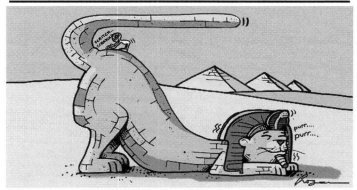

"I know I promised you Filet Mignon, but would you settle for ground beef?"

People of Earth. I am using your primitive video program to avoid contracting the so-called Corona Virus.
Your planet will soon be assimilated by our superior intelli..

Not now, Beatrice! I'm in the middle of a group chat!

"The Earthling honors us with this hunting trophy as a gift. Retrieve the item from the ship so we may reciprocate.."

"I have chosen my spirit animal."

© 2019 CES www.grayzonecomics.com

"Evacuate Immediately! The ship's about to be breached!"

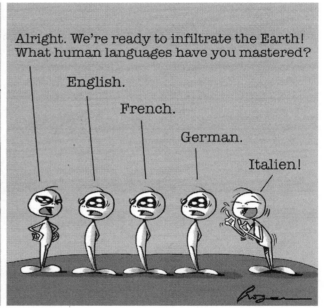

"I stocked the ship with a 90 day supply of donuts, Oreo and chocolate chip cookies, peanut butter & jelly sandwiches, Ovaltine and cold cereal. And well, I think you see where all of this is headed."

"I think it's time for a new ship. This one's got a comb-over."

I call it "Bloch Ness."

"According to her profile, she's an Olympic swimmer, former fashion model, graduate of Harvard with a degree in science who stands 5' 11" tall and is only 21 years of age. Perfect for our new alien/human hybrid breeding program!"

"That's what I love about you. Doesn't matter how old you get, you'll always have that kid inside you!"

"What a delightful turn of events!"

"Who kicked the back of my chair?"

"Nice Llanding!"

"I read that wrong. It says that they love *BOXES*."

"Ah...my masterpiece is finally complete!"

"Perfect...another 4-point landing."

Thanks!

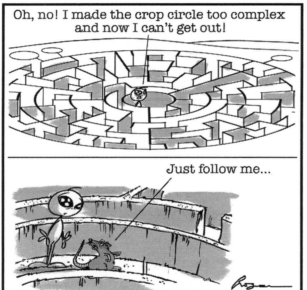

"In the future, it'll be known as Falconry."

Sweet ride!

Toucan play at that game!

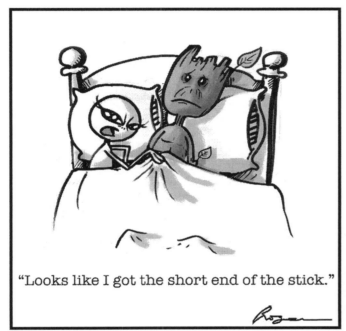

"Looks like I got the short end of the stick."

"Sorry, guys. This is my first year social distancing."

"I was just making crop circles in a marijuana field when I hit a pot hole."

"Typo."

"I think I found the source of the leak."

"Gesundheit!"

I grew weary of the weak beverage the humans dare to call "coffee" so I decided to use all of the advanced technology at our disposal to create a drink worthy of the name.

I harvested Earth's entire supply of java beans, roasted them upon the surface of the sun, compressed them all together within the crushing heart of a massive black hole and brewed it all using a colossal machine powered by the infinite force of dark energy!

...Let me know what you think.

Needs a little milk...

"Something for our Boys in Blue!"

Mothership, we have captured the Easter Bunny. Can you hear me? Come in Mothership. Do you copy? Are you there? Hello Mothership. Do you copy?

Try boosting the signal.

Copy that, Mothership. You're coming in loud & clear! Over!

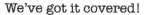

OK, listen up... Agents Simoni, Urbino, Bardi and DaVinci are assigned to Earth invasion project "Splinter." Since we all look alike, we need a way to tell each other apart...Any ideas?

We've got it covered!

"Sorry, there must be some mistake."

Landau Calrissian

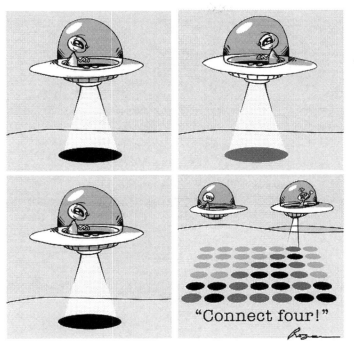

"Connect four!"

"Where is everybody?"

"Closer!"

"I always upload Data to the cloud."

"...and now, we wait."

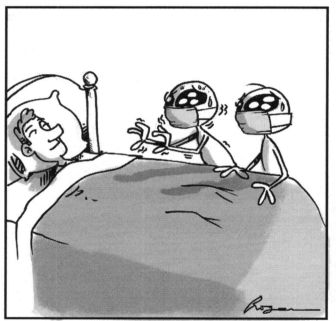 

"Why are we wasting our time fly fishing in the middle of a big city?"

"We're gonna need a bigger net."

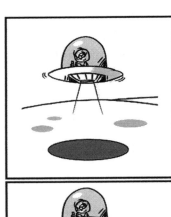

"What do you think about the theory that chickens evolved from dinosaurs?"

"Sounds plausible."

"I claim this planet in the name of the people of Mars!"

"Sir...we've discovered signs of intelligent life!"

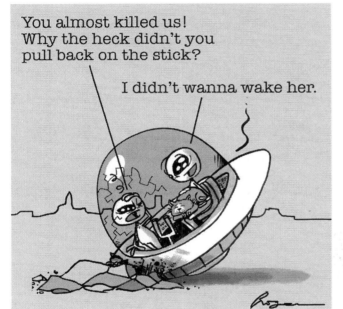

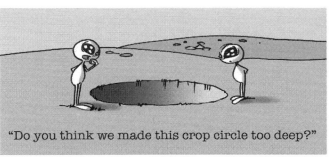

"Do you think we made this crop circle too deep?"

"Yes."

"Gnarly, dude!"

"What was that group of birds called again?"

"That's the problem with you Earthlings...
Always in need of assistance from others."

"Little help here!"

"This should freak out the future archaeologists!"

"He was a huge fan of D&D."

"I just sprung forward, there's no way I'm falling back!"

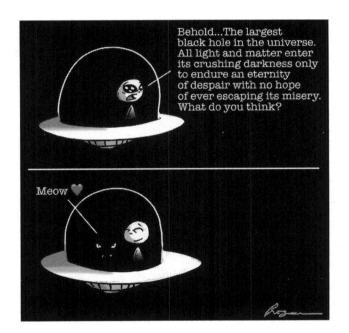

"Looks funny, works great!"

"Nice!"

"Ha! Ha! Ha! Your head looks human-sized!"

Receiving an incoming transmission with the following coordinates:

India - 22
Oscar - 17
November - 41
Golf - 13
Bravo - 51

BINGO!

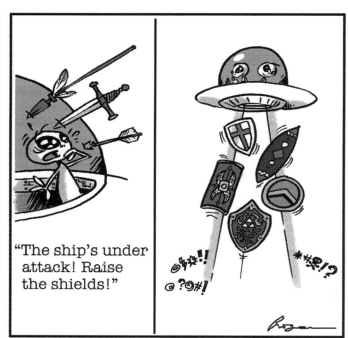

"The ship's under attack! Raise the shields!"

"I knew we should've used my mechanic!"

"Waiting for the humans to make contact."

"Look. I don't mind helping you get into and out of your ship while the tractor beam is out but if you yell 'Yabba Dabba Doo' one more time, I'm outta here!"

"It's an order to cease and desist."

"Keep looking. That jellyfish couldn't have gone far!"

"At least the crack's not in my line-of-sight."

Pardon me...
Would you have
any Grey Poupon?

Not yet!

"That's odd. When I first got him, he wouldn't shut up!"

"Menkaure."

"Khafre."

"Khufu."

"Locutus."

"Hey, guys, we're getting kind of close to the Sun, don't you think? Hey, guys....guys? Hello?"

"This one's more about quantity over quality."

"Only one creature is capable of doing this to our ship..."

"The Dairy Godmother!"

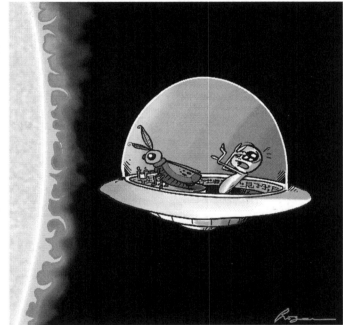

The windshield is really icing up. I can hardly see!

Gee, thanks...

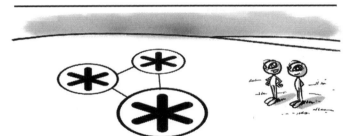

"I was just sitting by my computer when inspiration struck!"

"Marco!"

"Look...a Mercedes-Bends!"

"This guy really makes me want to step up my game!"

"I am Groot! I am Groot! I am Groot!""

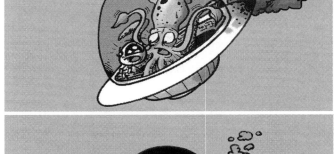

"Like I said, I only abduct name brand."

"Can you describe them?"

"I like 'em Chicago style!"

"Tonight, we sits like kings!"

"How does that Kringle guy stay so clean?"

"Umm...*Empire Strikes Back*? Hello?"

"Did it suddenly get warm in here?"

Ever since the divorce I managed to get in shape and now I feel amazing!

That's wonderful! How did you manage to do all that?

By dropping 100 pounds of unsightly fat!

"I got tired of waiting."

Oh, my God, Mildred.
You look amazing.
What's your secret?

I'm on a crash diet.

AAAAH!!! Aaaah! aaaa?

ah...

I was bitten by a spider!

I was bitten by a bat!

I was bitten by a wolf!

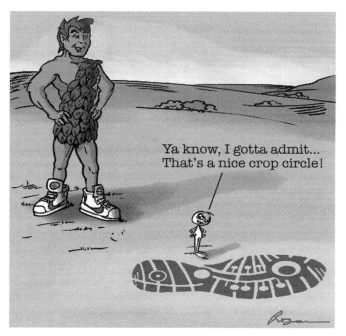

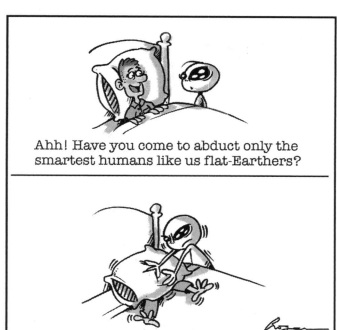

"The 80s called. They want their crop circles back!"

"Humans think *everything* is a touch screen!"

"If you don't like it, fix the tractor beam!"

"OK, listen up. Our mission here on Earth is to provide the humans with unlimited clean energy, restore their natural environment and help them end all the wars."

"Forget what I just said. We're just gonna take their cows!"

"Me no feel so good."

"I'm a big fan of your work!"

"I ordered an A and you sent me a Double D!"

"10W-40! 10W-40!"

"Whoa! A cell phone almost hit us!"

"That was a close call!"

"Let's get a cat, I said. But oh, no...
Everyone has a cat, you said.
Let's get something more **exotic!**"

"We're out of cyan."

"Looks like he's enjoying the view!"

We've got all the materials for the pyramid. Now who's going to put it all together?

Don't worry. I found a guy!

"Hey, let's get out of here...
I think these may be soy beans."

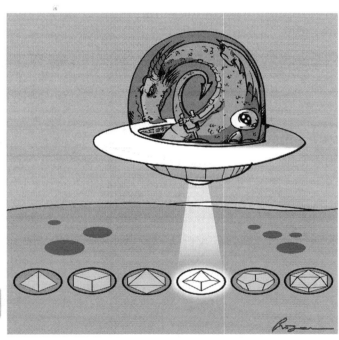

"E-F-P-T-O-Z."

Oh, no...the ship's broke again!

You mean the ship's "broken?"

No, it hasn't worked in three months!

Can I borrow five bucks?

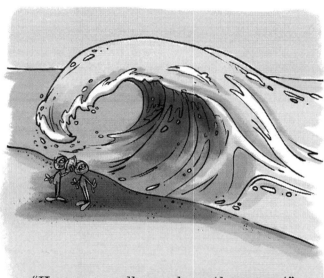

"Hey, you really *can* hear the ocean!"

"Improvise. Adapt. Overcome!"

"Man, those eyes just creep me out!"

"The tractor beam broke again,
so I had to improvise."

"That does it. No more hitchhikers!"

"This is *not* going to end well."

"Are you sure you're ready for another? You barely touched that one!"

"Hard soil."

"My legs are falling asleep."

We abducted you because centuries ago we eliminated the entire male population on our home planet. However, we soon realized that we need men for one specific purpose...

To help repopulate your home world?

God no! Just open this darn pickle jar.

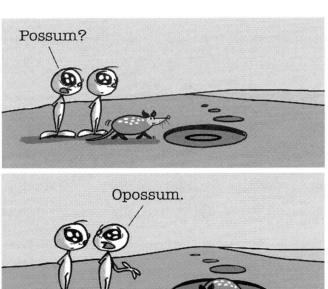

Being abducted by aliens isn't so bad...Your ship is really comfortable!

Yep. It came with every option I wanted...

...except leather.

We're entering an asteroid field...
We'll be smashed to smithereens!

OPEN THE HATCH, LITTLE ALIEN...
I'VE BEEN WAITING MY ENTIRE LIFE
FOR THIS VERY MOMENT...

You modified the tractor beam?

Why go to them when they can come to us!

"That constellation is Canis Major or The Great Dog."

"Virgo, of course..."

"That's Carina which is Latin for the keel of a ship."

"...and Crux, the Southern Cross."

Who would break up such a masterpiece?

"I'd like to buy a bowel!"

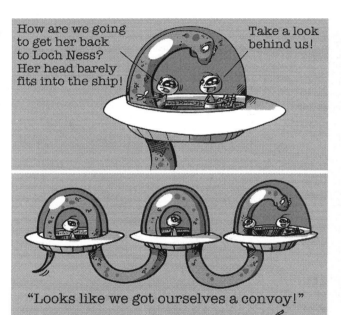

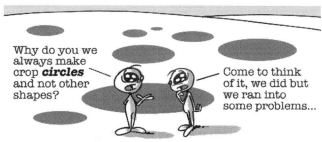

"I've been hit. You'll need to hack into the computer and land the ship!"

Parot Cards

"Miss Muffet ain't getting away this time!"

"Now I know why you guys don't fly."

"Did you guys happen to see which way a spaceship was headed?"

Ah, I see it. Thanks!

"You play winner!"

"On second thought, maybe I'll just take you back home."

"Sorry. Tractor beam's busted!"

I still don't see the star you're talking about.

I told you. It's the faint one below that bright one. You really need to learn how to see past your eyes!

Did someone say "pasteurize?"

"Alright...keep your eyes peeled for a heavily mustachioed plumber."

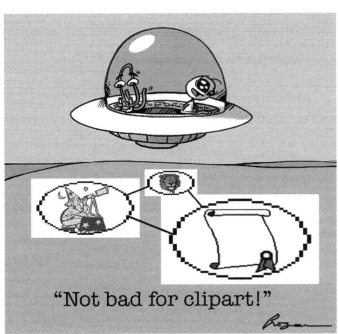

And now to sneak in and abduct him!

shiff..
schuff...
shiff...
shuff..

He got away! Why must you always wear corduroy?

"You just HAD to mention the ejector seat, didn't you?!"

"This is by far the most magnificent and beautiful creature in the entire galaxy! I must show my friend who is currently working ten years into the past."

"They say it's good for the skin!"

"We're about to enter Uranus."

"To be fair, we *did* evolve from humans."

"Well?!?"

"Giggity."

"I'm glad I crashed my ship here on Earth.
Back on my home planet we're all Atheists."

"Hit the deck! We're under fire!"

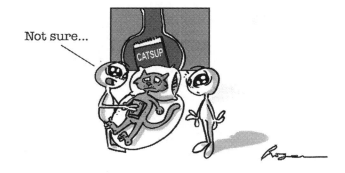

"Dali...get your butt down here!"

"Costco."

"Oooh, mighty orb of infinite knowledge and wisdom... will you tell us in which shape to build the sacred tombs?"

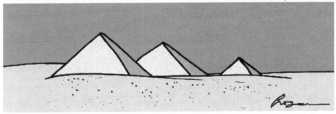

"An Earthling approaches us bearing gifts!"

"It's a DVD player and a gift card to Olive Garden."

"In order to make the ultimate guacamole, the avocado must be just right. If you take the ship ahead just one minute in time, it should be perfectly ripe."

"*@#%&*!! Go back 20 seconds!"

Leaning Tower of Giza

"Great work, guys. Who's the author?"

"Sorry your order is taking so long.
We're a little shorthanded."

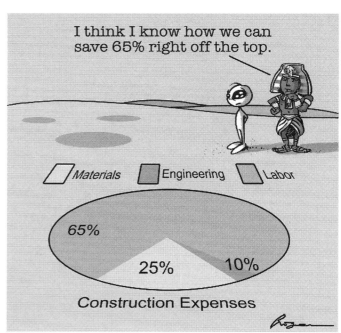

"YOU tell her it's not an egg!"

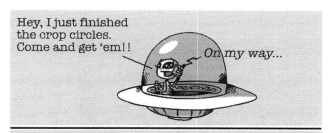

"Get our lawyer on the phone!"

"...and for the discerning man on a budget,
may I suggest one of our older models."

The next star system is 277,491.73 light years away.

It's more like 200,000...

...as the crow flies!

"That last asteroid we sent was way too small and only managed to kill off the dinosaurs. This giant one will destroy ALL life on Earth!"

"Guess again, losers!!"

"...and in last place..."

"All these guys are useless."

"Earth's atmosphere is dangerous to our species. Be sure to initiate advanced safety protocols."

"Pharaoh was a fan of Devo."

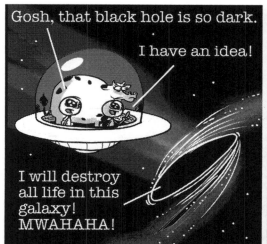

"More Wasabi!"

"Take me!"

"Well, unless you can think of a better idea,
this'll have to do 'til we fix the cloaking device."

"Much better than the red one! What did you use, an L.E.D.?"

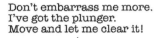

Gross...that really smells. You really clogged it up this time and I really needed to go. Why did you have to take such a big one?

Don't embarrass me more. I've got the plunger. Move and let me clear it!

"I can't believe you got me **ANOTHER TIE** for Christmas!"

"There was icing on the wings."

"Don't worry...I know a guy."

SubarUFO

"Just think of them as space heaters."

"Last year the cranberry sauce dried out before we even got home."

"It really is a very nicely detailed crop circle, but why is it raised?"

"That's an odd looking eclipse."

"Oh, man. I'm out of bubble wrap.
I need to find something else ..."

"Wow! Second base on the *first date!*"

"This is gonna be a looooong day."

"Unidentified, my ass!"

I have a kilogram of 20 centimeter long bananas
for you back at ship. They're being stored
at 4° centigrade. It's about 3 kilometers back.
Look for a saucer that's about 5 meters wide.

"He ordered a soy latte!"

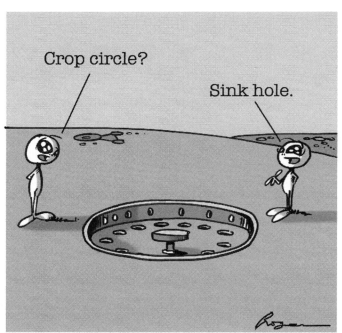

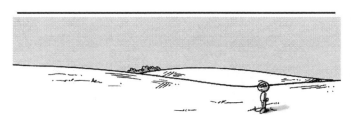

"Another perfect landing!"

"Remember to make it look like an accident."

So Long, and Thanks for All the Cows.

Made in the USA
Middletown, DE
29 August 2021